Happy Thoughts
My Little Journal

Open Your Heart!

This journal belongs to:

_____

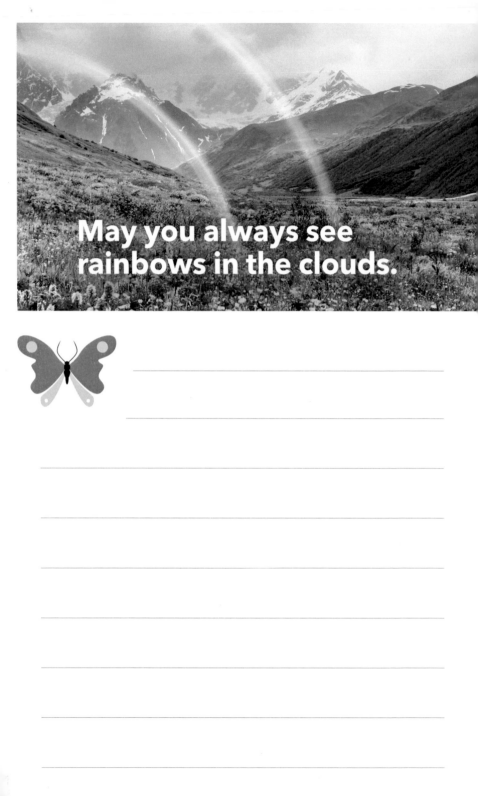

May you always see
rainbows in the clouds.

Smile

Be yourself.

Be grateful for

friends.

april 1, 2009
Sertified Swiftie15
Taylor5wift

Dance

like no one sees you.

Look for love.

Sharing is caring.

You don't have to be perfect

to be amazing.

If you can dream it

you can make it happen.

Take
one day

at a
time.

You can do it.

You are brave.

It's not what happens to you

it's how you handle it.

Imagine

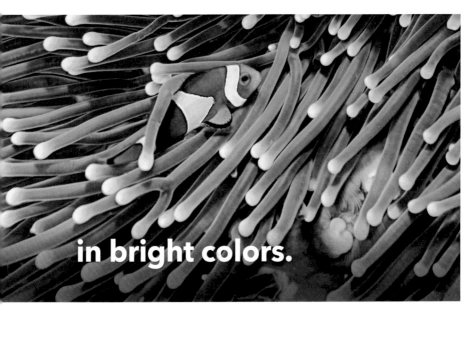

in bright colors.

_____

_____

_____

_____

_____   _____

_____   _____

_____

_____

_____

Don't look back

you're not going that way.

**Be strong
when you
are scared.**

Be brave when you are weak.

Stay connected.

You are loved.

_____

_____

_____

_____

_____

_____

_____

_____

_____

Believe in yourself.

Think positive.

Your dream
is nearer than
you think.

You are blessed.

Open your heart.

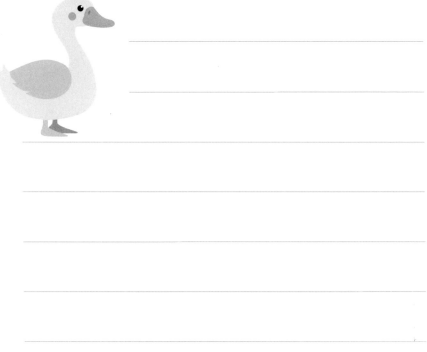

You are special.

Hope is real

and is
always here.

Stay calm.

Be forgiving.

You are
your own
person.

Never give up.

Hang in there.

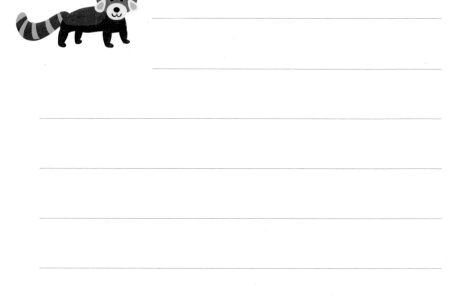

Be flexible.

Be kind to others

and learn from each other.

You are not alone.

**Hug
someone
you love.**

Life is tough

and so are you.

Never compare yourself to others.

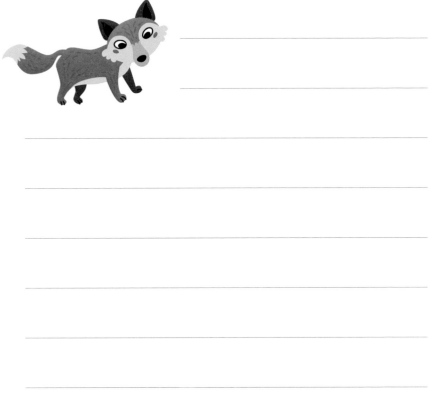

You are perfect.

Believe in magic.

Discover joy.

Be confident.

Reach for the stars.

HEALING NOTES

HEALING NOTES

About the Foundation   www.LightOfHealingHope.org

The Light of Healing Hope Foundation is a 501 (c)(3) charitable organization dedicated to providing books of hope as gifts to hospitals to comfort patients and their families at a time of adversity.

LHHF has made gifts to hospitals and hospices nationwide including Johns Hopkins, NIH, Walter Reed National Military Medical Center, The Washington Home and Community Hospices, and INOVA Hospitals.

We are committed to bringing comfort to all those who are suffering by offering pathways to spiritual hope, peace, and healing.

First published in the United States of America in 2021 by Light of Healing Hope Foundation

Art Direction and Design: Alexandra Villard de Borchgrave
Design: Henrique Siblesz, enlinea design
Stock Photography: © Alamy, Dreamstime, iStock, and Shutterstock

Printed and bound in the United States by Quality Graphics Printing Inc.
10 9 8 7 6 5 4 3 2 1
Library of Congress Cataloging-in-Publication Data

De Borchgrave, Alexandra Villard; Camel-Toueg, Jennifer
Happy Thoughts: My Little Journal — 2nd ed.
ISBN: 978-0-9914418-8-4